MW00632561

The M1 Abrams Main Battle Tank is the newest generation main battle tank used by the United States. It is named after General Creighton Abrams, a Battalion Commander during World War II under General Patton in the 4th Armored Division, and Army Chief of Staff and Commander of the U.S. forces in Vietnam from 1968-1972. The M1 entered service in 1980 and replaced the M60 series tank. The main versions of the Abrams tank include the M1, the M1IP, the M1A1 and the M1A2.

M1A2

The M1A2 was a further improvement of the M1A1 that consisted of a number of upgrades based on lessons learned in combat, including a commander's independent thermal viewer, improved commander's weapon station, position navigation equipment, and a full set of controls and displays linked by a digital data bus. These upgrades also included an improved fire control system. Work was done to improve the A2 model to an A3, but instead the variant took on the nomenclature of the **M1A2 System Enhancement Package (SEP)**. These improvements added improved digital displays for digital color terrain maps for the commander of the vehicle and a drivers integrated display along with thermal imaging management system. Also added were Force Battle Command Brigade and Below (FBCB2) enemy and friendly force tracking computing capabilities, and an improved cooling system to compensate for heat generated by the additional computer systems. The M1A2 SEP also serves as the basis for the M104 Wolverine heavy assault bridge.

The M1A2 SEPv2 (version 2) added Common Remotely Operated Weapon Station (CROWS or CROWS II) support, color displays, better interfaces, a new electronic operating system, better front and side armor, and an upgraded transmission for better reliability and durability. Further upgrades included depleted uranium armor for all variants, a system overhaul that returns all A1s to like-new condition (M1A1 AIM), a digital enhancement package for the A1 (M1A1D), and a commonality program to standardize parts between the U.S. Army and the Marine Corps (M1A1HC).

Weaponry

The main gun armament on the M1A2 is the M256A1 120 mm smooth bore gun which is a German design by Rheinmetall AG. This L/44 gun is a variant of the same 120mm smoothbore gun used on the Leopard 2's , up through the Leopard 2A5. The vehicle carries a variety of ammunition types. The M829A3 Armor-Piercing Fin-Stabilized Discarding-Sabot (APFSDS) round is designed to penetrate the best armor on any fielded tank today.

The 120mm M830 HEAT round is used primarily against lightly armored targets and field fortifications. In its secondary role it is used against personnel and armored vehicles. Each projectile consists of a steel body with a standoff spike. Inside the projectile is a cone copper liner and wave shaper which forms the explosives into a shaped charge for deeper penetration of the target. Finally, a crush switch in the nose and a switch on the shoulder of the projectile comprise the Full Frontal Impact Switch Assembly. When closed, any of these switches can activate the detonation sequencing.

The 120-mm M830A1 MPAT round is a fin-stabilized round that contains a HE warhead equipped with a selectable proximity switch and fuze that allows it to be fired in either AIR or GROUND mode. Its primary targets are light-armored ground targets, which are engaged with the fuze set to GROUND mode, allowing the round to function either when it strikes a target with a direct or glancing blow. It may also be used against bunkers, buildings, the flank and rear of enemy tanks, and enemy personnel.

The Abrams can also fire the M1028 120mm canister round, containing 1,098 deadly 3/8 inch tungsten balls, which has an effect similar to a large shotgun. An M908 bunker busting round is similar to the M830A1 except it has a steel head that allows penetration of the fortification before detonation.

Secondary weaponry includes the M240 machine gun, mounted in front of the loader's hatch, which fires 7.62 mm rounds. Some of these weapons had gun shields mounted around the loader to protect him when in combat. A second M240 is used as a coaxial gun to the right of the main gun. A third machinegun is mounted in the Commander's Weapon Station, usually an M2A1 .50 caliber MG, and can be fired from within the tank.

TUSK Upgrades

The Tank Urban Survival Kit (TUSK) is a series of improvements to the M1 Abrams intended to improve fighting ability in urban environments. These improvements were derived from lessons learned on the battlefield in Iraq and Afghanistan. Historically, urban areas and other close-in battlefields have been terrible places for tanks to fight. Typically, a tank's front armor is much thicker than that on the sides, top, or rear. The M1A2 tank is no exception. In an urban environment, attacks can come from any direction, using a variety of anti-tank guided missiles (ATGMs) or other tank-immobilizing devices, and attackers can get close enough to reliably hit weak points in the tank's armor or gain sufficient elevation to hit the top armor. A bad guy with an ATGM from a second story building can spell disaster for an Abrams rolling down a narrow street.

As part of the TUSK package, armor upgrades include reactive armor on the sides of the tank and slat armor (similar to that on the Stryker) on the rear to protect against rocket-propelled grenades (RPGs) and other shaped charge warheads. A Transparent Armor Gun Shield and a thermal sight system are added to the loader's top-mounted M240B 7.62 mm machine gun, and a Kongsberg Gruppen Remote Weapon Turret carrying a .50 caliber machine gun (again similar to that used on the Stryker) is in place of the tank commander's original .50 caliber machine gun mount. An exterior telephone on the rear of the tank allows supporting infantry to communicate with the tank commander.

The TUSK system can be installed in the field, so tanks can be upgraded without being recalled to a maintenance depot. While the reactive armor may not be needed in many situations, for general maneuver warfare, items like the rear slat armor, loader's gun shield, infantry phone (which saw use on tanks as early as World War II and back on USMC vehicles in the early 2000s), and Kongsberg Remote Weapons Station for the .50 in caliber machine gun will be added to the entire M1A2 fleet over time.

M1A2 with TUSK Modifications

Remote weapons station

Loader's Armor Gun Shield

Loader's thermal sight

tank/infantry telephone

Thermal sight goggles

Rear protecting unit slat armor

Thermal sight components

Abrams Reactive Armore Tiles

United States Department of Defense, Public Domain

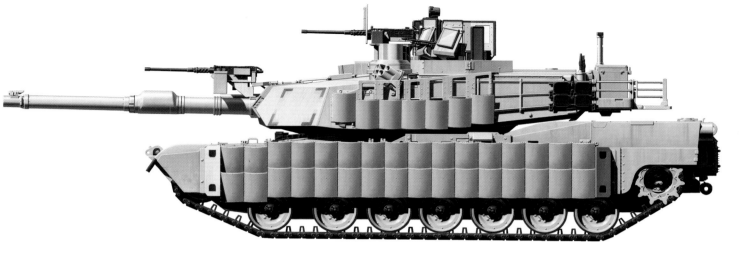

M1A2 SEP v2 with TUSK in Iraq

III/2/3 ACR, E-66 in Iraq, 2010-2011

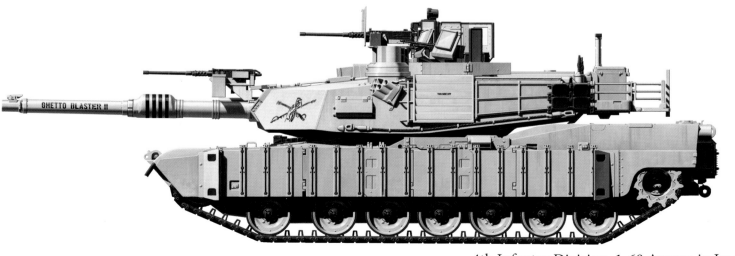

4th Infantry Division, 1-68 Armor, in Iraq

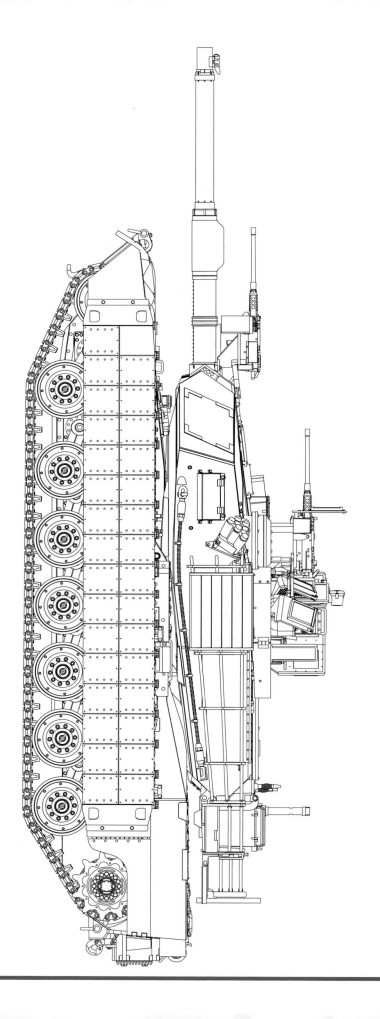

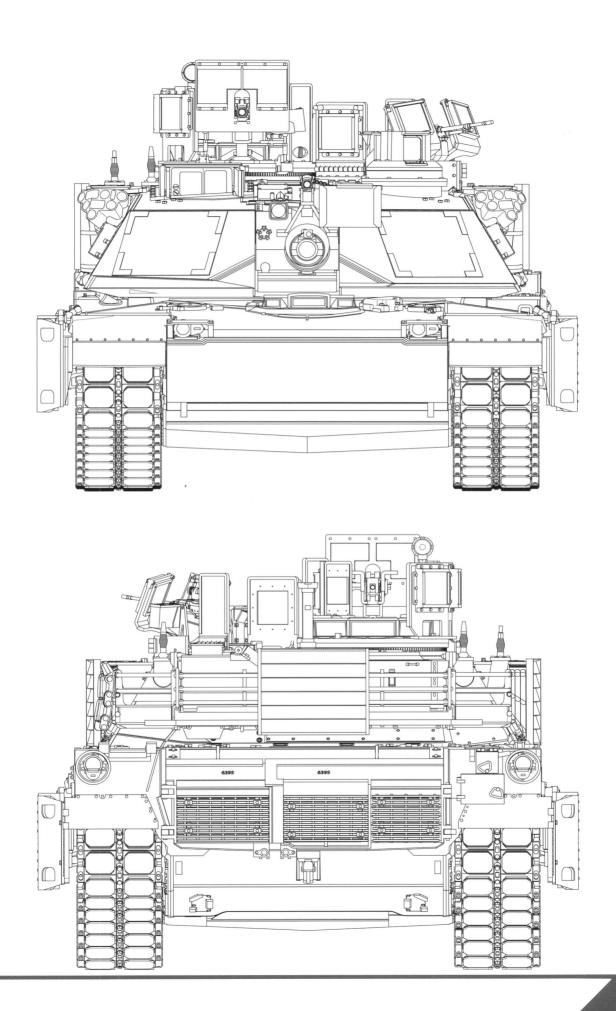

ABOVE: At the end of a long day, a tank crew from 3-8 Cavalry, 1st Cavalry Division, conducts after operations maintenance as the sun sets in the Middle East. This M1A2 SEP has a mine roller adapter mounted on the hull. BELOW: Tankers roll back out on patrol after refueling at Joint Security Station Sadr in Baghdad. The tankers of Company D, 2nd Brigade Combat Team, 3rd Infantry Division, currently attached to 3rd Brigade Combat Team, 4th Infantry Division, Multi-National Division – Baghdad, returned to their patrols mere minutes after their arrival.

An Abrams Tank from 3rd Squadron. 3rd Armored Cavalry Regiment, drives up an onramp of a highway in Mosul, Iraq.

Soldiers from 1st Combined Arms Battalion, 68th Armor Regiment, 3rd Brigade Combat Team, 4th Infantry Division, Multi-National Division – Baghdad, maneuver an M1A2 Abrams tank as they return to Combat Outpost Ford, after a mission in northern Baghdad.

M1A2 with TUSK. Tank E-66, with the 2nd Squadron, 3rd Armored Cavalry Regiment in Iraq.

Soldiers of C Company, 1st BN, 68th Armor Regiment, 3rd BCT, 4th Infantry Division, conduct gunnery training with the M240 and the M2 .50 caliber machine guns.

VENTRE A TERRE

Images of the M1A2 SEP v2 from 1-77 Armor, 4th Brigade, 1st Armored Division. Photos courtesy of Jim Patrick.

Images of the M1A2 SEP from 3-8 Cavalry, 1st Cavalry Division. Photos courtesy of Rosendo Varela. Several images are of vehicles from the 3-8 Cavalry that were rotated to Korea to become 3-8 Cavalry 2nd Infantry Division.

Photos courtesy of Rosendo Varela.

Photos courtesy of Rosendo Varela.

Photos courtesy of Rosendo Varela.

Soldiers from 3rd Platoon, Company C, 1st Combined Arms Battalion, 68th Armor Regiment, 3rd Brigade Combat Team, 4th Infantry Division, Multi-National Division - Baghdad, on board an M1A2 Abrams tank, make their re-entry to Combat Outpost Ford, after a mission in northern Baghdad.

An M1A2 from 3rd Armored Cavalry Regiment M1A2 in Iraq. This is an older SEP that used the Enhanced Position Locating Radio System (EPLRS) versus the Blue Force Tracker (BFT) system.

A U.S. Army soldier from Bandit Troop, Tiger Squadron, 3rd Armored Cavalry Regiment bore sight the M1A2 Abrams tank before moving onto range 11 to fire practice rounds at Besmaya Range Complex in the Iraqi Army side of Forward Operating Base Hammer in Wasit, Iraq. (U.S. Army)

An M1A2 from Delta Company "Dark Knights," 3rd Battalion, 69th Armor Regiment, 1st Armor Brigade Combat Team, 3rd Infantry Division cross a vehicle launched bridge provided by engineers of the Royal Netherlands Army during exercise Heidesturm Shock near Storkau, Germany, June 6, 2015.

An M1A2 Abrams main battle tank from the Minnesota National Guard races through a breach in a barbed wire obstacle during the 116th eXportable Combat Training Exercise at the Orchard Combat Training Center, Idaho. (U.S. Army photo by Sgt. Leon Cook, 20th Public Affairs Detachment)

Soldiers with 1st Armored Brigade Combat Team, attached to 5th Squadron, 7th Cavalry Regiment, stationed at Fort Stewart, Ga., pose for a photo in front of an M1A2 SEPV2 Abram Tank during a field training exercise at Novo Selo Training Center, Bulgaria, Nov. 17, 2015. (U.S. Army photo by Staff Sgt. Steven M. Colvin/Released)

M1A2SEP V2 tank ammo loader of 1st Armored Brigade Combat Team looks at the distant targets through his binoculars, as the gunner, who sits inside the Abrams tank, controls the M101 Common Remotely Operated Weapon Station (CROWS) during a field training exercise at Novo Selo Training Center, Bulgaria, Nov. 17, 2015. (U.S. Army photo by Staff Sgt. Steven M. Colvin/Released)

Soldiers of 1st Armored Brigade Combat Team, attached to 5th Squadron, 7th Cavalry Regiment, 3rd Infantry Division, stationed at Fort Stewart, GA, close the turret hatches of an M1A2 SEP2 Abrams Tank to begin their field exercise training in support of Operation Atlantic Resolve at Novo Selo Training Center, Bulgaria, November 17, 2015. (U.S. Army photo by Staff Sgt. Steven M. Colvin)

Soldiers assigned to the 2nd "Stallion" Battalion, 8th Cavalry Regiment, 1st "Ironhorse" Brigade Combat Team, 1st Cavalry Division, prepare an M1A2 Abrams tank for a firing iteration during the Stallion's fall gunnery, at Fort Hood, Texas. (U.S. Army photo by Pfc. Paige Pendleton, 1st BCT PAO, 1st Cav. Div.)

An M1A2 Abrams tank rolls through a cleared mine obstacle while a Bradley Fighting Vehicle provides security during a breach training exercise, Nov. 1. The 2nd Battalion, 69th Armored Regiment, 3rd Heavy Brigade Combat Team, 3rd Infantry Division conducts the training as part of Hammer Focus, the brigade's largest field exercise at Fort Benning, GA.

U.S. Army M1A2 Abrams tanks arrive at the Grafenwoehr Training Area, January 31, 2014. The vehicles are part of the European Activity Set, a combined-arms battalion-sized set of vehicles and equipment prepositioned at the Grafenwoehr Training Area designed to support the U.S. Army's European Rotational Force and the NATO Response Force during training exercises and real-world missions. (U.S. Army photo by Markus Rauchenberger)

U.S. Army Soldiers from 1st Brigade, 1st Infantry Division plow a path in a breach clearing Abrams Tank at the National Training Center on Fort Irwin, Ca., April 20, 2014.

U.S. Soldiers, assigned to 2nd Battalion, 5th Cavalry Regiment, 1st Brigade Combat Team, 1st Cavalry Division, maneuver M1A2 Abrams tanks to the Rose Barracks (Vilseck), Germany, railhead station May 5, 2014, as part of Combined Resolve II, a U.S. Army Europe-directed multinational exercise at the Grafenwoehr and Hohenfels Training Areas, including more than 4,000 participants from 13 allied and partner countries. (U.S. Army Photo by Visual Information Specialist Gertrud Zach/Released)

2nd Battalion, 5th Cavalry Regiment, 1st Brigade Combat Team, 1st Cavalry Division at Hohenfels Army base during a capabilities day presentation prior to the start of Combined Resolve II.

SGT Resha (right) and Spc. Michael Shiver work together to refuel an Abrams tank at Joint Security Station Sadr in Baghdad. (U.S. Army photo/Sgt. Mark Matthews)

Soldiers of 5th Squadron, 7th Cavalry Regiment, 3rd Infantry Division, stationed at Fort Stewart, Ga., drive a camouflaged an M1A2 SEP2 Abrams tank during Exercise Peace Sentinel at Novo Selo Training Center, Bulgaria, November 23, 2015. (Photo by Staff Sgt. Steven M. Colvin)

An ammunition loader of an Abrams M1A2 SEP, works with the tank, gunner to align the weapon system and sights prior to conducting the qualifying live-fire exercise at Orchard Training Center near Boise, Idaho.

A tank with 2nd Battalion, 5th Cavalry Regiment, 1st Brigade Combat Team, 1st Cavalry Division engages targets during the combined arms live fire exercise at Grafenwoehr Army Base, Germany. (U.S. Army photo by Spc. Marcus Floyd, 7th Mobile Public Affairs Detachment)

Tank crewmen are performing the all-important maintenance on a M1A2 SEP. The crewmen are cleaning the tank's main gun AKA "punching the guntube" between missions.

An M1A2 Abrams tank crew with Company D, 2nd Battalion, 9th Infantry (Mechanized), 1st Armored Brigade Combat Team, 2nd Infantry Division, conduct pre-checks before heading out to the range March 3 at Rodriguez Live Fire Complex.

M1A2 SEP (possibly a V3) firing at the Orchard Combat Training Center in Gowan Field, Idaho. The stepladder on the turret of the SEP in the lower picture is to allow a crewman to look through the muzzle boresight device in the main gun prior to starting gunnery training (see the top photograph on page 30).

An Iraqi army officer takes aim with a .50-caliber M2 machine gun during a live-fire demonstration at Besmaya Range, adjacent to Forward Operating Base Hammer, Iraq.

ABOVE: Soldiers assigned to 1st Squadron, 1st Cavalry Regiment, 2nd Brigade Combat Team, 1st Armored Division prep an M1A2 Abrams tank in the Fort Bliss training areas near Orogrande, NM, during Iron Focus 17 May 10, 2017. BELOW: An M1A2 from 2nd Battalion, 7th Infantry Regiment, 1st Armored Brigade Combat Team, 3rd Infantry Division conduct Gunnery Table XII live-fire exercise May 9, 2017 on Fort Stewart, GA.

M1A2 engine pack pulled and lying on the floor in the back of the vehicle. This pack has just been cleaned. Photo courtesy of Rob Cogan.

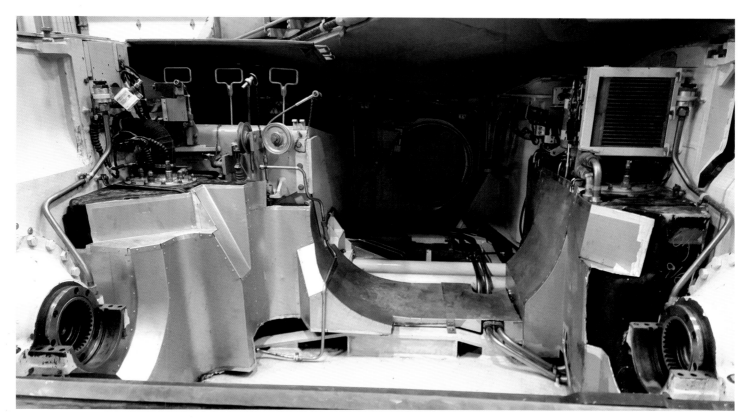

M1A2 engine compartment without the engine. This area has just been cleaned. Photo courtesy of Rob Cogan.

An M1A2 SEP that supports the US Army Armor School at Fort Benning Georgia. This tank was on display for a tour of Fort Benning by the Armor Modeling and Preservation society in April 2013. The brown panels on the front of the turret are Combat Identification Panels (CIPs) which will give a reverse polarity image in friendly vehicles main gun sights when the panel is flipped over.

Shown to advantage is the #1 skirt on the SEP. As all SEP tanks are rebuilt M1/M1 Improved Product (IP) tanks, they lack the original serial number tags that were attached during the initial production and removed during the rebuild process. Also, the wear on the T-158LL track center guides is apparent.

The side view of the SEP. Shown are the rest of the skirts, the NBC over-pressurization unit on the hull as well as the M250 smoke grenade launchers and ready grenade boxes, the side CIPs which have the 45 degree angled slats that allow the "no power thermal" tape to give the reverse polarity image when viewed through thermal sights. Also, on the roof of the turret, the Commander's Independent Thermal Viewer (CITV) is shown.

The rear side view of the SEP tank. Several features can be seen here. First is the scalloped sprocket, which saves some weight over the earlier sprockets, and the mud relief holes that thankfully, model companies have been including in the recent M1 series tank models. Also visible is the door to the second battery compartment that replaced the second hull fuel cell found on M1 and M1A1 tanks

ABOVE: A side view of a Ft Hood based M1A2 SEP from C Company 3-8 Cavalry, 1st Cavalry Division. There are loads of details shown in this and following photos that represent a tank in an operational unit.

BELOW: Rear oblique. Of the SEP at Ft Hood. Note the slave cables wrapped around the M250 Smoke Grenade Launcher and missing extra grenade box. Additionally, the right side #7 skirt and mudflap are also missing. Photos courtesy of SSG Rosendo Varela.

ABOVE: The tank's tow bar is mounted on the front attachment points via clevises. The exhaust deflector is in the bustle rack extension and the track rope is wrapped around the upper bars of the extension. The skirts are open to allow the crew to conduct track and suspension maintenance.

BELOW: Front oblique view. The tank has a chock block under the track at the #1 roadwheel "just in case". The white end connector is a mark to the tank crew that that particular end connector requires additional attention as it has been added or loosened recently. Tankers can live or die by the constant maintenance that their tanks require. Photos courtesy of SSG Rosendo Varela.

Two overall photos of the 3-8 Cavalry M1A2 SEP at Ft Hood Texas. Notice the differences in appearances between it and the Armor School tanks at Ft Benning, Georgia. Note the white painted end connector on this side of the SEP. My guess is that the tank recently received a new set of track pads recently. Photos courtesy of SSG Rosendo Varela.

A couple of side views of an M1A2 SEP with the TUSK I kit installed. The fittings on the side of the turret in the lower picture are for the TUSK II mounting plate for the curved armored tiles to protect the turret. (Photos by John Charvat)

Several more detail pictures of the TUSK equipped M1A2 SEP. Note that the TUSK II brackets run to the front of the turret. (Photos by John Charvat)

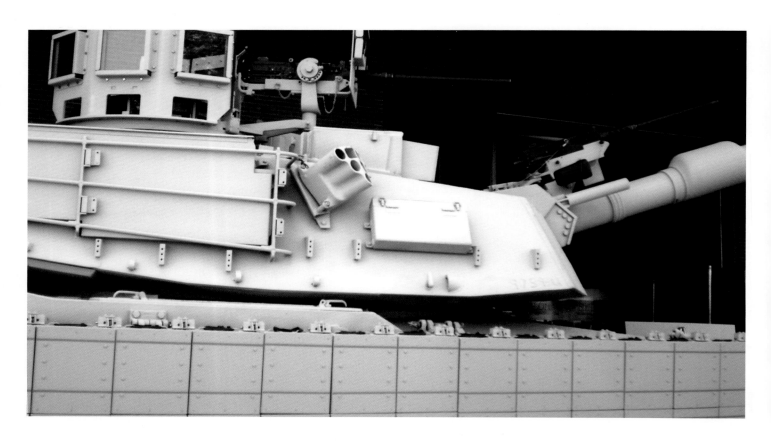

ABOVE: More details of the TUSK equipped M1A2 SEP at the 2007 Armor Conference at Ft Knox, Kentucky. Note the high powered light that is mounted on the side of the Counter Sniper /Anti Material mount (CSAMM) that allows a second M2 .50 Caliber MG to be mounted above the main gun.

LEFT: A close up of the Tank Commander's (TC) protective armor that is part of the TUSK. Despite the adding of the extra armor, the US Army decided to add the CROWS 2 Remote Weapon Station to further increase the protection of the TC by allowing the use of the system from inside of the armor of the tank. (Photos by John Charvat)

ABOVE: Close up details of the TUSK 1 equipped SEP. The olive straps on top of the ARAT are handles to assist with the installation of the tiles. Once the tiles are positioned on the attachment rails, rails, the fittings on the top of the rails hold the tiles in place.

LEFT: A shot of the SEP before the Armor Conference opened as shown by the machine guns laying on the top of the turret and hull. This tank is a rebuilt M1 or M1IP tank as it retained its original vertical light guards. (Photos by John Charvat)

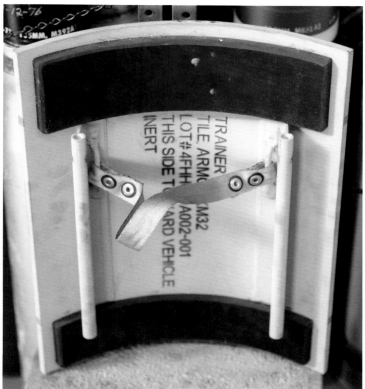

The training XM32 ARAT that make up the TUSK 2 armor package that was used in Iraq. These curved tiles were added to the XM19 tiles (seen in the bottom picture) as well as to the sides of the turret to give deployed Abrams tanks added protection from insurgent weapons.

The tank line in the Company C 3-8 Cavalry motorpool at Ft Hood Texas. Note the sand paint jobs, green replacement parts and loader's gun shields. The tactical markings on the skirt depicts the far recognition for the tank: the upward pointing echelon= 1st Platoon, the 2 = 3-8 Cavalry, and the 3 = C Company.

An elevated side view of a M1A2 SEP V2 at Ft. Benning in April 2013. The BFT antenna is mounted alongside of the Gunner's Primary Sight cover. The tank behind is a SEP V3 as it has the CROWS 2 mounted on the turret.

An oblique side view of the SEP. The Slave Receptacle and TIP boxes are on the right rear of the tank. Looking upward the new style Antenna Matching Unit (AMU) which uses a smaller metallic whip antenna, instead of the older eight foot tall fiberglass antenna found on Cold War era vehicles.

The right sprocket and number 7 skirt of the SEP. The skirt is held in place by a pin that connects the skirt to the rear mud flap. Both are made out of aluminum as a weight saving measure. The number 7 skirt is often removed to ensure that mud buildup clears the sprocket. The four bolt hub cover in the center of the sprocket covers a quick disconnect linkage to allow the tank to be towed by another tank or M88 Recovery Vehicle without damaging the transmission.

The rear view of the M1A2 SEP. This vehicle is equipped with additional batteries, used for powering the turret when the engine is off. M1A2s and early production SEPs had a small turbine power unit in the left sponson in the hull and an exhaust vent between the left tail light and the left grill door. The power unit was found to be unreliable and were replaced with the extra batteries found on this example. On the right side are the slave cable (jumper cables) receptacle box and underneath, the Tank Infantry Phone (TIP) box. Inside is a phone on a retractable cord that allows infantry accompanying the tank to talk to the crew without exposing themselves or the tank crew to hostile fire. The two plastic containers are to catch any lubricants that leak from the vehicle.

A close-up of the engine grill door of the SEP. The rusted center vent and grill is the Lycoming ATG-1500 turbine engine exhaust while the right as well as the left (not shown here) vents and grill are for the transmission cooler exhaust. The grills that lie in front of the vents assist in diverting the exhaust horizontally away from the tank. Below the grill door is the vehicle tow pintle.

Detail shots of the weathering of the M1A2 SEP exhaust grill as well as a tarp covered turret face with black Velcro starting to separate from the armor. The runs and drips are from the surface preparation spray, which helps the glue on the velcro strips stick better to the tank's armor.

A collage of detail and weathering – chipping detail shots of the back of a M1A2 SEP. The small box is the external slave receptacle (think jumper cables) while the larger one is the Tank Infantry Phone box.

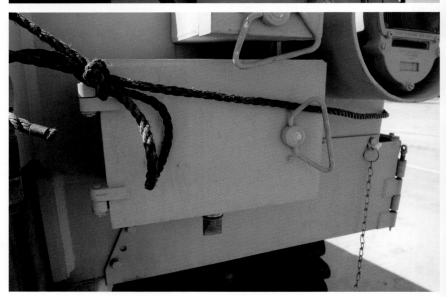

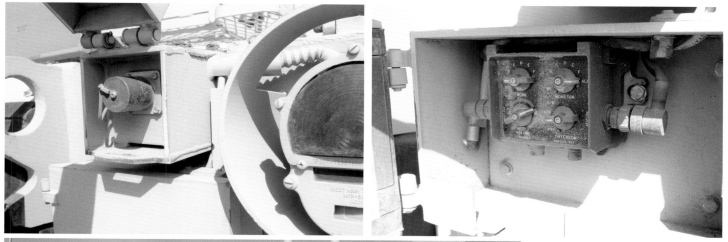

A series of rear oblique pictures of the display SEP at Ft Benning in April 2013. The center pictures provide detail shots of the open external Slave Receptacle and Tank Infantry Phone boxes.

The driver in his "hole". The M1A2 SEP's driver, like all M1 series tanks, is in a semi-reclined position to lower the tank's overall profile. Since the turret is reversed, the driver entered the tank from the Loader's hatch. Whenever the tank has the gun forward, the driver should have his hatch closed to prevent injury or more likely death.

Training tanks get a bit beaten up… Damaged but still serviceable fenders on two Armor School tanks. The flexing of the aluminum fenders causes the Chemical Agent Resistant Coating (CARC) paint to pop off. Most parts come in either Army Green or Tan, depending on what part number is ordered.

A rather worn M1A2 SEP at Ft Benning. An interesting thing about this tank is that is does not wear the usual hull ballistic skirts, instead, has the thinner ones that are used to mount the Abrams Reactive Armor Tiles (ARAT) that was added to M1A1s and M1A2 SEPS in Iraq from 2006-2011. The tank to the right has a Loader's and Tank Commander's gun shields mounted. The dark soot is from the vehicle running through an area that was subject to a range fire a few days earlier.

ABOVE: A tank commander, wearing protective goggles and gloves is surveying the battlefield. The BFT antenna, with the black cover is attached to the Gunner's Primary Sight (GPS) cover on this particular SEP V2.

BELOW: A close up of the Driver's Hatch and the laser reflective vision blocks, which were introduced to the Armor force in the mid 1990's as a result of the increased use of battlefield lasers, fielded by the Soviets in the 1980's and used by both sides in the 1980-1988 Iran-Iraq War.

More hull and fender detail shots. Fenders and mud flaps are not always immediately replaced as seen by the notations on the mud flaps. Tanks get beat up from new drivers and/or tank commanders who have not gotten a feel for the performance of the M1A2 SEP.

The fender retaining spring with a T-158LL track end connector. This is a normal procedure as when conducting track maintenance, the fender spring is unlatched from the small angle fitting in front of the end connector, the fender is lifted up and the end connector is flipped over to hold the fender up and allow the crew a clear view of the upper side of the track. Note the rough anti-skid coating and the Military Load Class 70 marking at the lower right corner. The M1A2 SEP weighs 70 tons when it is fully loaded with ammunition, fuel, and crew equipment.

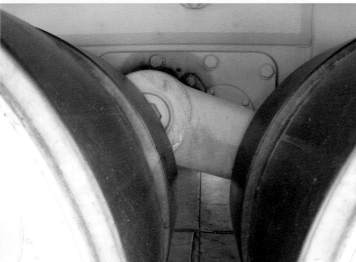

Detail shots of the SEP's suspension. The clear hubs for the roadwheels are a new design that none of the current model makers have reproduced – yet.

Detailed T-158LL track and SEP suspension photos. The difference between the older T-158 track and the current T-158LL is that the LL track has skeletonized center guides (not guide horns) to reduce weight. Note the coloring on the tracks as well as the new rust on the sprocket. That tank has been moved recently. The lower three pictures show a SEP that is missing the aluminum mud flap as well as one with the mud flap in place.

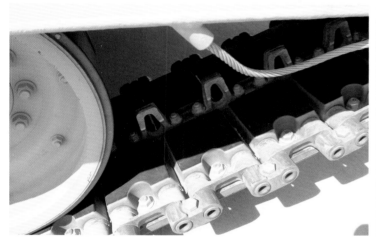

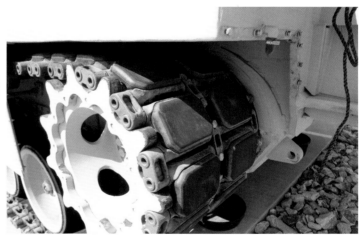

ABOVE: Detail shots behind the tank skirts, showing the compensating idler, which allows the adjustment of the tank's tracks tighter or looser. The support roller, on the right side, supports the track as it continues around the upper part of the track run forward to the idler wheel and then to make contact with the ground at the #1 road-wheel.

The belly of the M1A2 SEP. The hull is an all steel welded construction without a belly escape hatch. The Tank Urban Survivability Kit (TUSK) provides a V-shaped under hull armor package that can be added to the tank to provide additional protection from under hull detonations from Improvised Explosive Devices (IEDs) or mines.

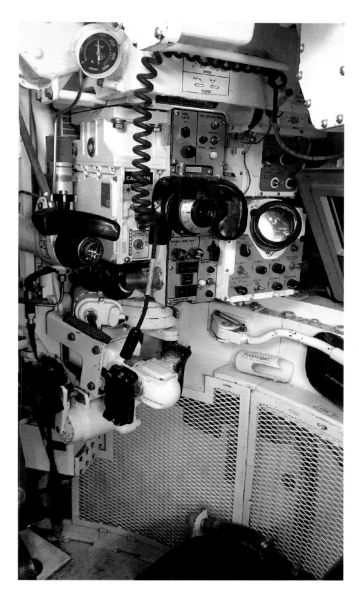

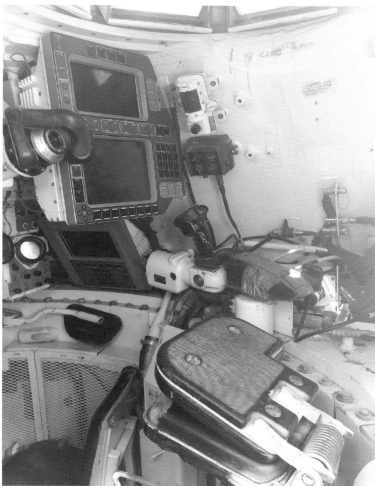

Inside the turret of the M1A2. The gunner's station is above, to the left. The commander's station is the above right photo. The 120mm gun breech is to the right.

Inside the turret of the M1A2. Both photos above are of the commander's station. The photo below is driver's hole.

Inside the turret of the M1A2. The photos above are of the loader's station. The left photo is the area where the loader sits, while the right photo is the loader's view of the turret in his position. Below is a panoramic view of the commander's and loader's stations.

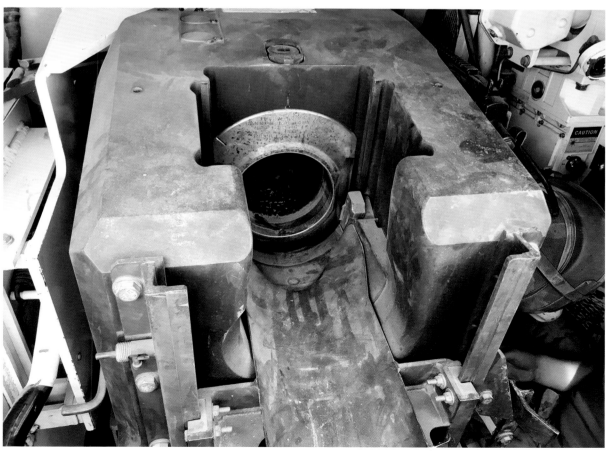

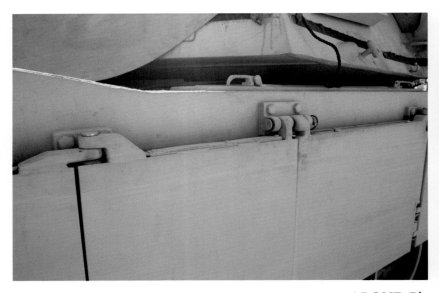

ABOVE: Photos showing hull details on the SEP tank: hull stowage box lid, the bilge pump outlet (2 pictures) as well as the heater exhaust that is forward of the overpressure unit.

BELOW: Soldiers of A Troop, 1st Squadron, 3rd Armored Cavalry Regiment, prepare their M1A2 Abrams tank to fire on the Besmaya Combat Training Center range near Baghdad (U.S. Army) Note the mix of uniforms, the TC in the older olive Combat Vehicle Crewmen (CVC) overalls and the newer Army Universal Camouflage Pattern (UCP) digital pattern Outer Tactical Vest (OTV)and with the groin protector flap., while the Loader has a complete set of UCP coveralls, vest and the UCP gray-green balakava.

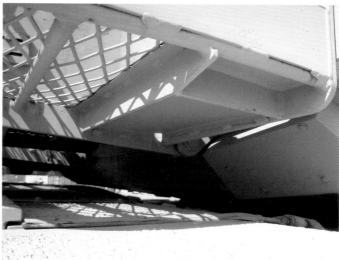

Detailed pictures of the rear of the SEP turret: a close up of the side of the bustle rack extension, the main bustle rack lower attachment points, the tow cable sleeve attachment point.

ABOVE: Another frontal view of an Armor School M1A2 SEP. Judging from the scuff marks, this one is used regularly for training new Armor Soldiers and leaders.

MIDDLE and LEFT: Close ups of the underside of the main bustle rack and Vehicle Condenser System Unit (VCSU) exhaust, the ducting and the bustle extension rack and main bustle rack attachment points.

The back of the turret. The folding bustle rack extension was added to re-place the storage space that the VCSU now occupies in the main bustle rack. Five gallon jerry cans of water are usually strapped to the carriers on the outside of the rack.

Looking down on the turret. At the bottom of the picture is the top of the CITV and the Global Positioning System antenna which is mounted above the curved shield that protects the CITV optics when it is not in operation. Behind the CITV is the Loader's hatch, with the Loader's M240 7.62 mm machine gun, which is mounted on a pivoting mount as well as a skate ring. Typically the loader is responsible for observing the left rear of the tank.

Looking to the left rear of the SEP's turret, the VCSU is located in the SEP's bustle rack. Behind the VCSU is the folding bustle rack extension, which was added to make up for the loss of stowage space for the tank crew's combat equipment. Also shown are the access doors for the second battery compartment which replaced the earlier Under Armor Auxiliary Power Unit (UAAPU) that early M1A2 SEPs had mounted in place of the left rear fuel cell.

The right rear of the SEP turret. The armored box under the antenna mount is for the AN/ AKA the "Duke" Counter Radio controlled improvised explosive device Electronic Warfare system. The left antenna mount and the capped off mount for an Enhanced Position Location Reporting System (EPLRS) antenna, which looks like a thicker radio antenna. (Photo by John Charvat)

The M256 120mm main gun, in the stowed position over the back deck of the tank, which allows the driver access to his position from the turret hatches. The M240 coaxial shroud is the object in the lower left corner.

A good view of the CROWS 2 storage brackets for folding the unit down and securing it to the top of the turret for travel. Behind the brackets is the CITV in its stowed position.

A close up of the M153 CROWS 2 optics. The upper left is the daylight sight, lower center is the thermal sight, whose round cover is stowed on the side of the ammunition box and upper right is the laser range finder/pointer.

Another shot of the rear of the turret with a overall view of the CREW Armored box, the folded wind sensor, and the VCSU. We also have a sighting of the renowned modeler, photographer, and foodie, Christopher Mrosko.

Looking inside of the Loader's hatch, the bottom row of the 120 mm ready rack and the lower rail for the sliding ammunition blast door is visible. The ammunition door is normally closed and opens hydraulically via a knee switch that the tank loader uses to activate the door to gain access to the ammunition compartment. The M1A2 SEP carries 40 120 mm main gun rounds, with 17 in the ready rack, 17 in the semi ready rack and 6 in the hull ammunition compartment.

A detail shot of the front of the turret of a SEP. Not the roughness of the antiskid paint that was applied during the M1A2 SEP rebuild process. (Photos by John Charvat)

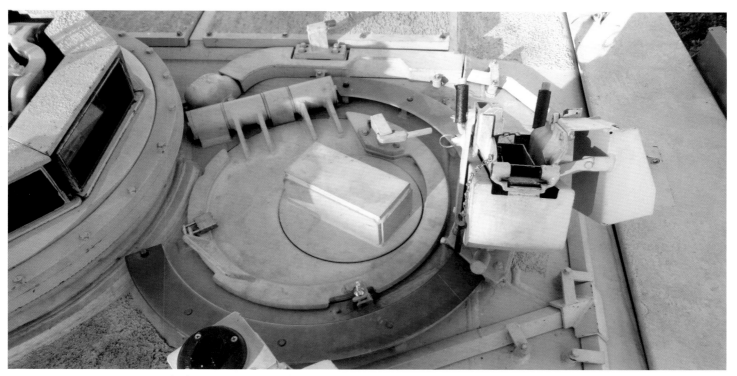

ABOVE: M1A2 SEP Loader's Hatch, Loader's M240 mount and the skate ring. The tank's Global Positioning System antenna is the black object at the base of the picture.

BELOW: The conduit which protects the wiring that provide power to the CSAMM system. The M240 coaxial MG blast tube is in the center of the photo. (Photos by John Charvat)

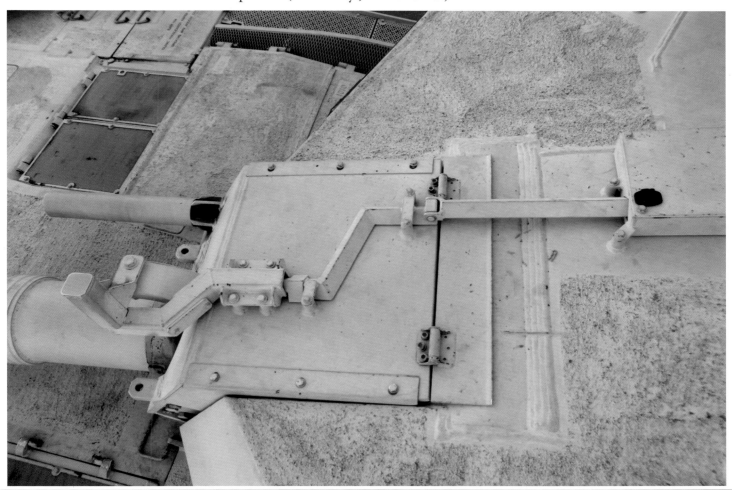

ABOVE: The SEP's Improved Commander's Weapon Station (ICWS) with the hatch in the closed position.

LEFT: The SEP's blow off panels. These are a protective feature, along with the sliding ammunition compartment door to protect the crew from any ammunition detonation by venting any explosions upward to blow off the panels and not allowing the force of the explosion into the turret. The round elevated areas were vents that were welded up when the vents showed no benefits to protecting the ammunition or crew. (Photos by John Charvat)

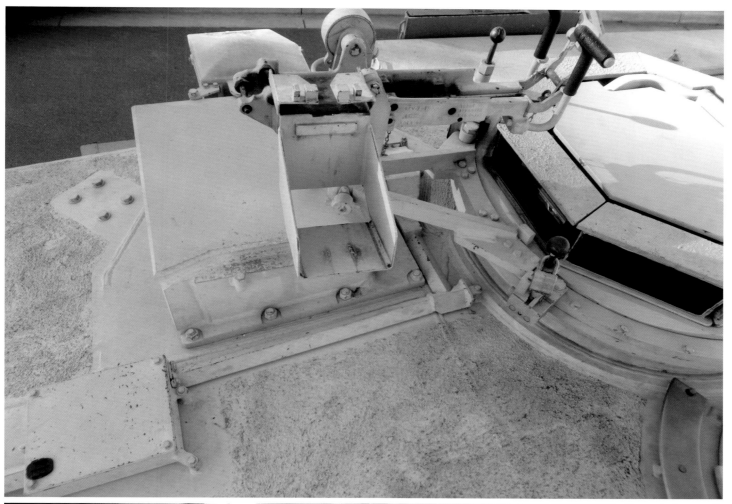

Detail shots of the ICWS and the GPS cover with the sight doors closed. The GPS cover has the BFT antenna mounted on the side of the cover. (Photos by John Charvat)

A couple of views of the TC armor panels for the M1A2 SEP TUSK. The black object is a hand held spot light, which is seen better in the lower picture. This was used by the TC to illuminate suspicious objects during night patrols. (Photos by John Charvat)

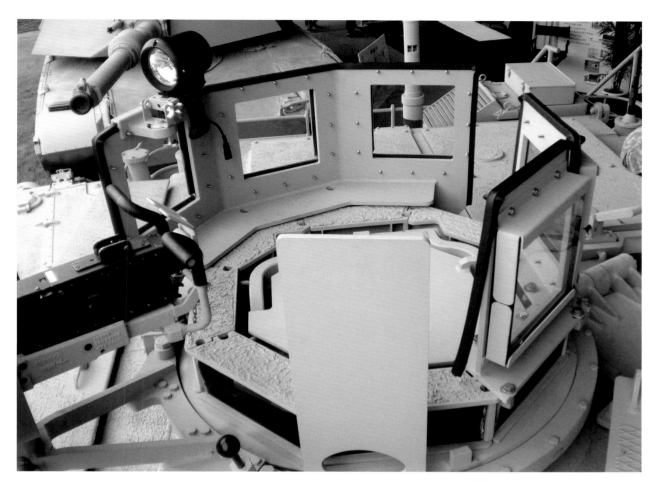

Additional ICWS with the TUSK Armor package. All of the glass panels are blast resistant and provide the TC with the ability to see what is occurring around him without exposing himself to hostile fire. (Photos by John Charvat)

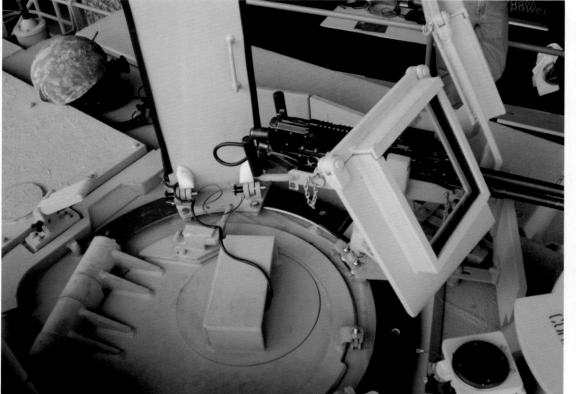

The Loader's position with the TUSK protective transparent armored gun shield for the M240 machine gun and additional armor panels to protect the loader. This also shows a Picatinny rail added to the feed tray cover. The loader's helmet in the background has a small thermal sight attached to increase the loader's ability to engage targets at night. (Photos by John Charvat)

Additional detail photos of the loader's M240 machine gun and the protective gun shield from the side and top views. The shield with the diamond mesh over the glass folds down, while the mesh protects the glass from errant feet stepping on it. (Photos by John Charvat)

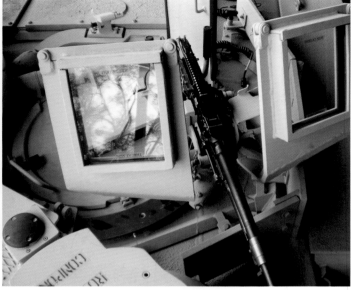
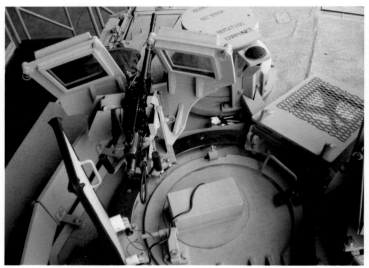
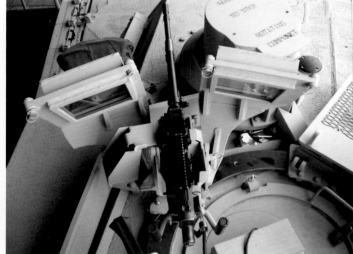

Additional detail photos of the loader's M240 machine gun and the protective gun shield from the side and top views. The shield with the diamond mesh over the glass folds down, while the mesh protects the glass from errant feet stepping on it. (Photos by John Charvat)

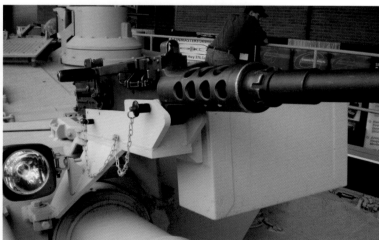

Detail photos of the Counter Sniper/Anti Material Mount (CSAMM) showing the .50 Caliber Browning machine gun mounted as well as the details of the mount with the MG not mounted. The weapon is manually charged and electrically fired, via the Gunner's power control handles. Note the spotlight that is mounted next to the weapon. (Photos by John Charvat)

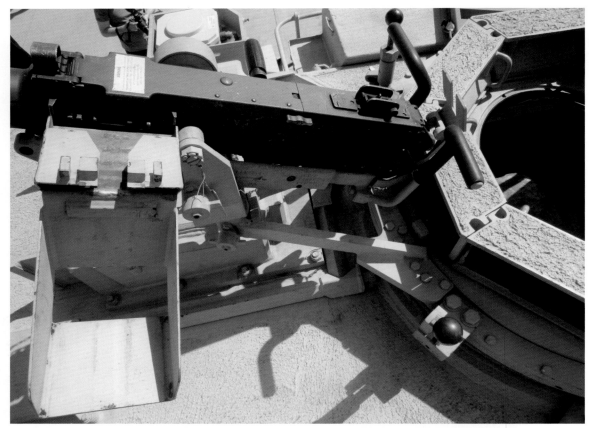

The receiver of the M2 .50 caliber machine gun mounted in the M1A2 SEP's Improved Commander's Weapon Station (ICWS). This machine gun differs from typical M2 MGs as it does not have the spade grip handles at the rear of the M2 receiver. Instead, the black handlebar assemblies allow the Tank Commander (TC) to control the weapon. The black knobs, on either side of the machine gun mount engage a locking mechanism to prevent the ICWS from traversing.

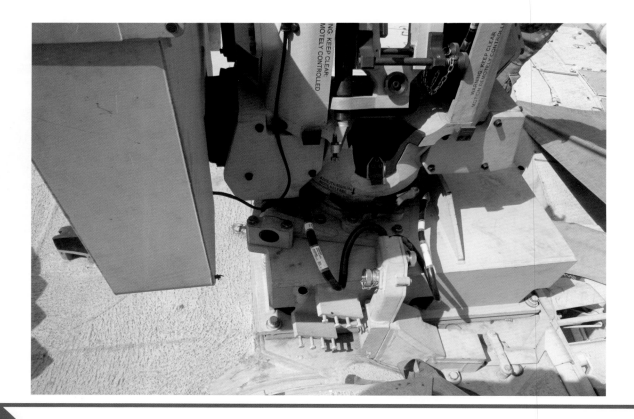

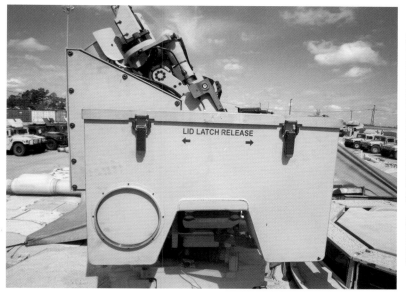

Several different detail shots of the left hand side of the CROWS 2. The upper right shows the hinge point used to "fold" the system into the rubber stowing mounts, shown in the middle left picture. The CROWS 2 is lowered during travel (ship, plane or train) to reduce the overall height of the tank. The lower pictures show the guards that protect the daylight and thermal sights as well as the laser range finder when the system is at zero degree elevation.

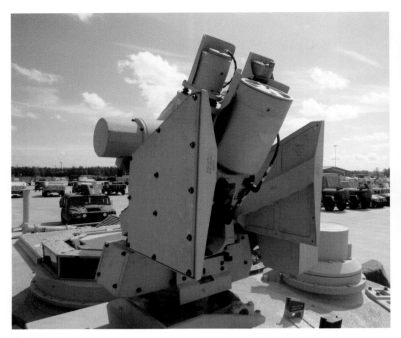

Detail shots of the CROWS 2, including the mount that fits above the armored Gunner's Primary Sight (GPS) housing.

The CROWS 2 fitting to the M1A2 SEP forced the Blue Force Tracker (BFT) antenna to be moved from the left side of the GPS cover backwards to the EPLRS antenna mast on the rear of the turret. The relocated BFT antenna is the black covered object behind the turret stowage box.

Several detail shots of the Loader's M240 Machine Gun and the mount. The M240 was introduced to the US Armor force in the early 1980's to replace the M73 and the later M219 7.62 mm machine guns, used on the M60 Series tanks.

Loader's M240 as well as one below of the M2 .50 Caliber machine gun. These pictures can be used to super detail any of the current M1A2 SEP models on the market.

A top down look at the GPS (left), the Tank Commander's .50 caliber in the ICWS , the conduits to protect the cabling going to the M250 Smoke Grenade launchers as well as from the BFT antenna (the white object at the top of the picture). Note how thick the anti-skid texturing is on the vision block guards on the ICWS.

The M1A2 SEP's M2 .50 Caliber Browning Machine Gun in the ICWS (top three pictures). The lower two show the conduits and junction boxes for the CSAMM to mount a second M2 machine gun over the SEP's main gun to use in situations where a 120mm main gun round may not be warranted against the intended target.

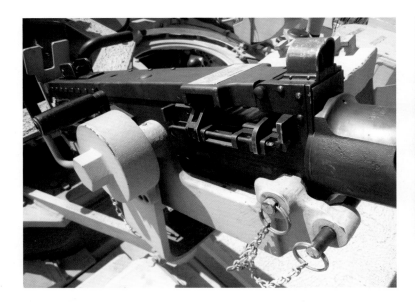

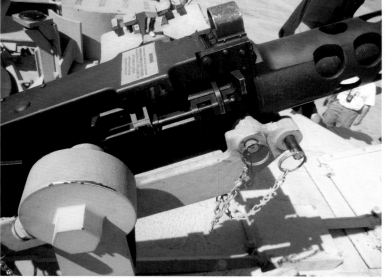

Additional ICWS pictures for super detailing purposes. This whole assembly will be removed when the M153 CROWS 2 Remote weapons station is fitted to the tank to make A M1A2 SEP V3.

The top of a M1A2 SEP turret from 1st Battalion 77th Armor, showing the GPS cover, with the attached Blue Fore Tracker antenna (darker tan object behind the GPS cover and the CSAMM conduits and junction box. The unit is conducting tank gunnery training at Ft Bliss Texas. Photos courtesy of Jim Patrick.

Close up of the inner ICWS hatch. The "T" handle disengages the hatch lock to allow the hatch to be angled to fully close it. The TC will grab the green strap to guide the hatch into the locked position and use the black handle to fully lock the hatch closed. Photo by Jim Patrick.

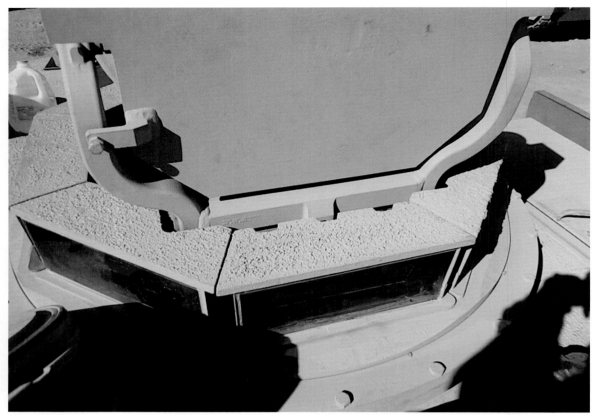

ABOVE: The rear of the ICWS hatch. The bracket on the side of the hinge arm limits the movement of the hatch to prevent injury to the TC. The eight vision blocks in the ICWS is an improvement over the six vision blocks found in the M1A1's Commander's Weapon Station.

BELOW: Close up of the ICWS. The gearing underneath the armored collar is for the .50 caliber machine gun mount to traverse to the left and right to engage targets.

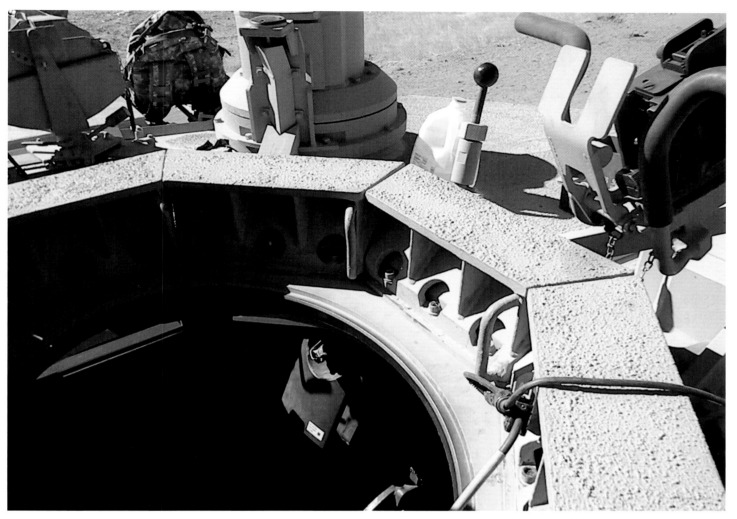

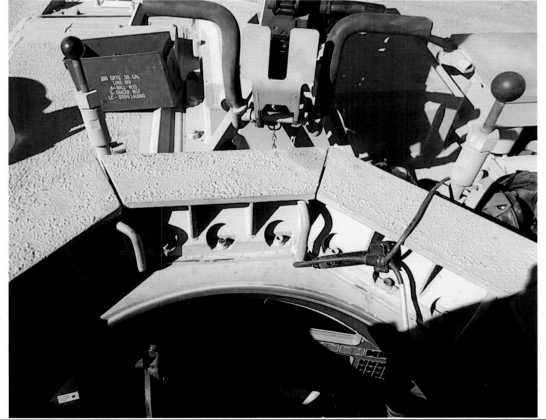

ABOVE: A view from the Tank Commander's ICWS, looking towards the right. The loader's MG mount is at the left, with the CITV in the center and the .50 caliber mg mount handles and butterfly triggers on the right.

LEFT: A view from the Tank Commander's ICWS, looking forward at the .50 handles, triggers and traverse locks. The empty .50 caliber MG Ammo box is being used to hold the expended brass and links, that drop from the weapon between the ICWS and the GPS cover.

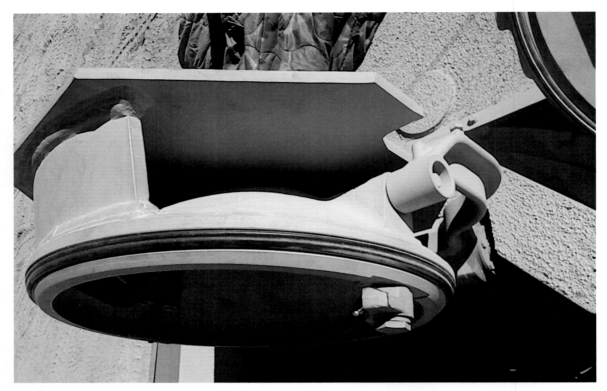

ABOVE: The ICWS hatch looking at it from the right side. It consists of an inner and outer hatch and a hinged arm to allow the TC to have the hatch in a closed, an open or open protected positions. The "open protected" hatch position has the hatch open slightly which allows the TC to look while being protected from overhead threats.

BELOW: A view of the ICWS from the left side. Note all of the crap (a technical term) that accumulates around the ICWS when the tank is in use.

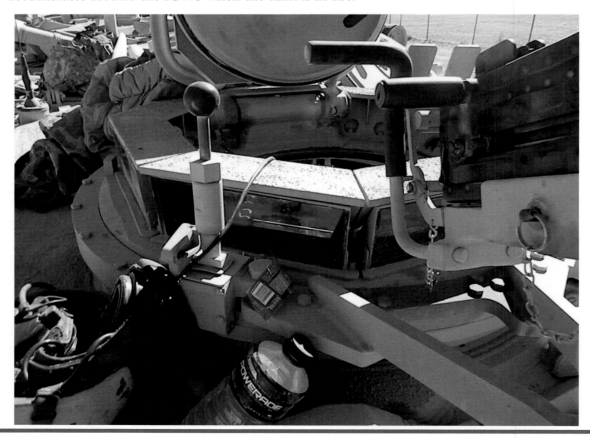

ABOVE: Another view of the ICWS, its forward vision blocks, the .50 caliber machine gun mount and the traversing lock, all shown to advantage here.

BELOW: Details of the TC's hatch hinge on the ICWS.

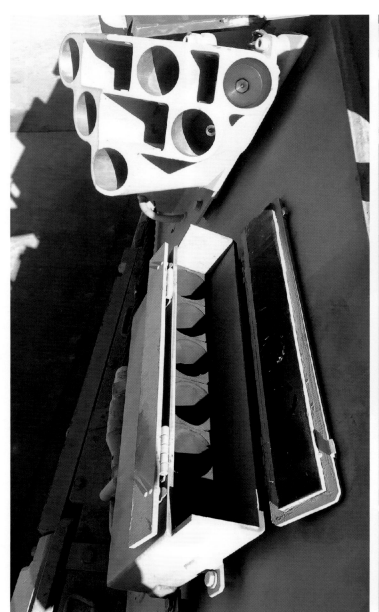

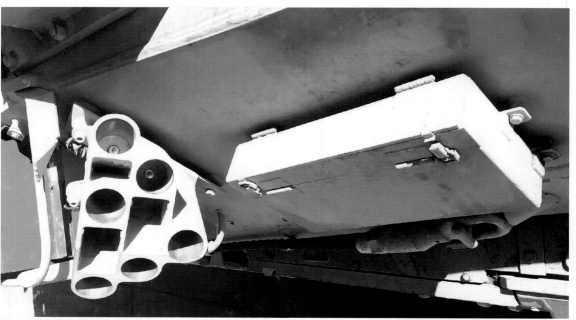

Detail shots of the British designed M250 Smoke Grenade Launchers and the spare ammo boxes. In the top right photo, it looks like some enterprising tank crew has decided to store grease tubes in place of the smoke grenades…

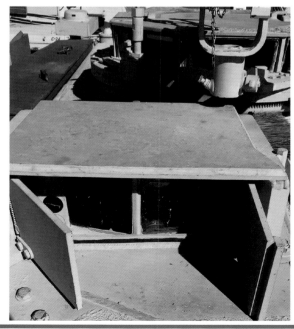

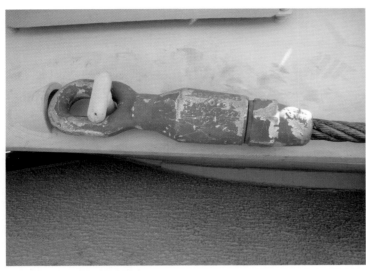
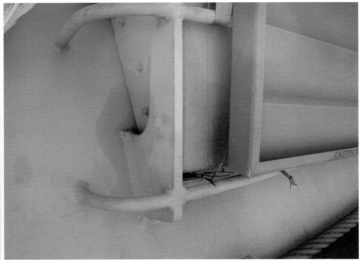

Detail shots of the turret box/turret rails and the tow cable stowage point. The rounded guard protects the cable from being ripped off while traveling through brush.

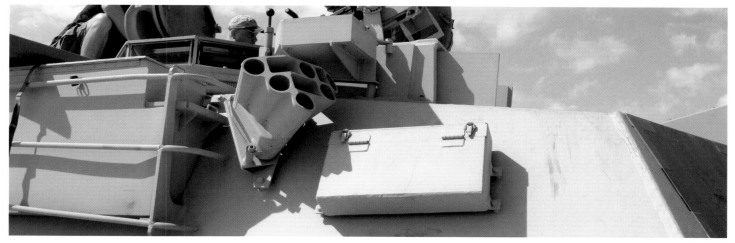

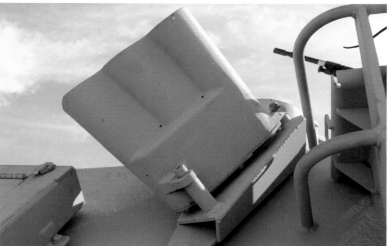

Detail shots of the M250 Smoke Grenade Launcher and its mounting brackets. Additionally, the details of the BFT antenna bracket/protective mount are shown to advantage.

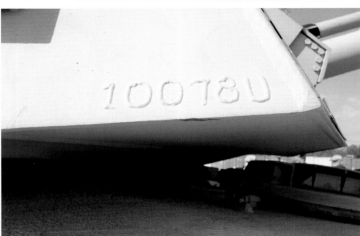

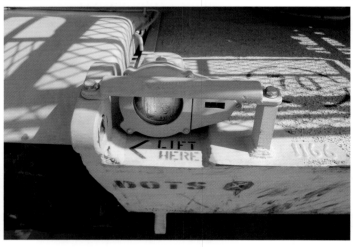

Detail shots of the tank's headlights as well as the factory applied turret number. By the headlight guards, this is a remanufactured M1 series tank hull with a late model "big" turret added during the conversion to a M1A2 SEP. Most M1 Improved Products (IP) and early M1A1s were converted to SEPs.

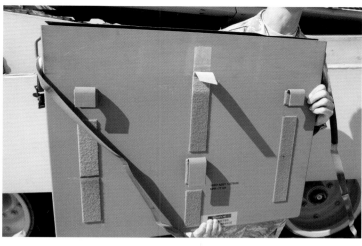

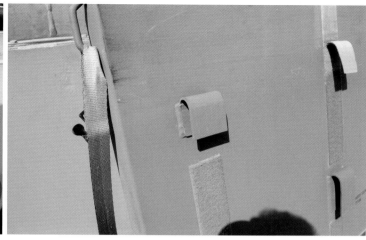

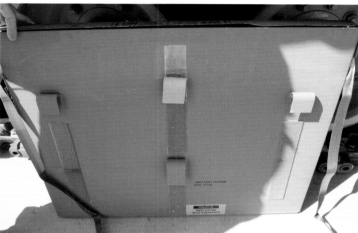

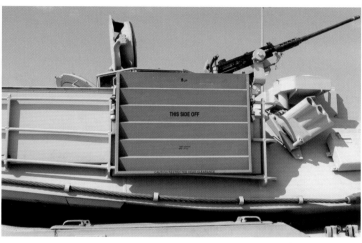

This series of pictures show the details on the Combat Identification Panel (CIP).

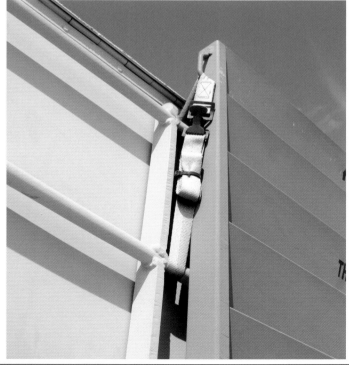

M1A2s Training in the Field

ABOVE: An electrically raised and lowered mine plow. It has a magnetic mine activating "dogbone" (black cylinder) with the added center mine rake. Each US Army tank company will have three of these systems as well as a mine roller to counter adversary minefields. This one belongs to 1st Platoon, C Company, 3-8 Cavalry, 1st Cavalry Division at Ft Hood Texas. BELOW: An M1A2 Main Battle Tank assigned to 1st Battalion, 35nd Armored Regiment breaches through obstacles during the Army Warfighting Assessment (AWA) 17.1 at Fort Bliss, Texas.

Aerial drone image of an M1A2 crew, from the 1st Armor Brigade Combat Team, 3rd Infantry Division, conducting Table VI Gunnery at Fort Stewart, GA, December 6, 2016.

Pages 102-103: U.S. Soldiers assigned to 1st Battalion, 64th Armor Regiment, 1st Brigade Combat Team, 3rd Infantry Division, assault an objective during Decisive Action Rotation 17-05 at the National Training Center in Fort Irwin, CA.

Page 104: BG John M. Epperly, 29th Infantry
Division Deputy Commander, visited with
Operation Spartan Shield troopers of 6th
Squadron, 9th Cavalry Regiment, 1st Cavalry
Division at Camp Buehring, Kuwait.

Page 105: Troopers of 6th Squadron, 9th
Cavalry Regiment, 1st Cavalry Division at
Camp Buehring, Kuwait. Note the artwork
painted on the commander's hatch.

Barracuda camouflage testing, Ft. Bliss, TX

The following two pages show an example of the Saab camouflage that is undergoing field evaluation with various units of the U.S. Army. This example is with 1-37 Armor, 1st Armored Division, at Ft.. Bliss, Texas. This mobile camouflage, made by the company's Barracuda business unit, is designed to provide camouflage as well as signature management. It is designed to reduce the chance of visual detection as well as detection by sensors, such as near infrared, short wave infrared and radar. The material is very durable, easy to use and may negate the need to repaint vehicles to match operational environments.

"C'mon Man" the nickname for C32, a M1A2 SEP from C Company, 1-64 Armor, prepares for its first defensive engagement from Battle Position 1 on the Red Cloud Multiple Purpose Range Complex (MPRC) at Fort Stewart Georgia. The Red Cloud MPRC is named for a Korean War Medal of Honor winner and allows for various types of weapons systems to conduct live fire training upon it, from dismounted infantry squads to tank platoons to AH64E attack helicopters.

ABOVE: C14, a SEP from C Company 2-7 Infantry, moves onto the MRPC with its weapon systems elevated and the gunner's primary sight doors closed as the crew is about to start its day run during the 1st Armored Brigade Combat Team's winter tank gunnery training. BELOW: Tank Crew load the vehicle's crew served weapons, the tank commander's M2A1 .50 caliber machine gun and the loader's M240 7.62mm machine gun as part of their gunnery preparations.

ABOVE: A D Co crewman bore sights his tank in the boresighting area of the Red Cloud MPRC at Ft Stewart. Boresighting allows the crew to align the tank's main and auxiliary sights with the muzzle of the main gun at a defined distance to increase the accuracy of the 120mm main gun. LEFT: A 3d Infantry Division tanker is removing the 200 round 7.62mm ammunition cans from its wooden packing crate. The mixed load of 120mm training rounds, .50 caliber and 7.62mm machine gun ammunition was brought to the range on a Pallet Loading System (PLS) flat rack.

ABOVE: C11, a C Company 2-7 IN M1A2 SEP known as "Can't Spell Lost" undergoes last minute repairs before being called forward to the ready line, as the crew prepares to negotiate the range. BELOW: C21, C Company 1-64 AR, scans downrange for targets the Red Cloud MPRC during the 1st ABCT winter gunnery at Ft Stewart, Georgia.

ABOVE: A close up of the tactical markings of a 3-69 Armor tank. The crew used "hundred mile an hour tape", the military equivalent of duct tape, for the temporary markings. The first number is the battalion designation, the second number the company, and the chevron is the platoon.
BELOW: A M1A2 SEP from 1st Armor Brigade Combat Team (ABCT), 3ID tank, with its turret draped with camouflage nets and the weapons systems elevates, sits on a concrete hardstand at the Red Cloud MPRC.

ABOVE: A M1A2 SEP sits on a concrete hardstand at the Red Cloud MPRC. The range tower that controls the targets as well as provides instructions to the firing vehicles is in the background. The rusted exhaust diverter is stored on the turret rails as a rather weak attempt of camouflage by using some natural flora as well as camouflage netting.

LEFT: This 3ID tank crew is "up in the hatches" before negotiating a Combined Arms Live Fire Exercise or CALFEX. The turret is plied with crew bags and the crew has made an attempt to camouflage the turret with pine branches as part of the tactical "play" of the CALFEX.

ABOVE: D22, from 1-64 Armor, is preparing for an offensive engagement during CALFEX gunnery training. During offensive engagements, tank crews are scored on the timing as well as accuracy of their weapons as they engage stationary and moving targets with main gun and machine guns. BELOW: Here is D22, after its CALFEX day run, with its turret reversed to the rear. The pine branches are inserted into easily accessible parts of the turret.

ABOVE: A missing left rear mud flap results in a mud splattered engine deck and skirts after this M1A2 SEP comes back to the MPRC hardstand after its day CALFEX run. This tank is probably D22, the tank first seen on the previous page.

LEFT: A close up of a M1A2 SEP turret, probably D22 from 1-64 Armor. The side of the turret is also covered with the same sandy mud that is seen in the picture above. These could be easily replicated on any one of the new 1-35th scale M1A2 SEP models.

ABOVE: Another M1A2 SEP, this one missing the left rear mud flap and the resulting mud build up on the rear of the tank.

RIGHT: D22, 1-64 Armor returns from their day CALFEX run. The weapons systems are elevated per the range standard operating procedures and the loader and tank commander are looking towards the company tank line and will attend an after-action review that focuses on the unit's actions during the run's series of engagements.

The pictures on this page show a tank crewman (loader) loading the main gun during an engagement during tank gunnery. The loader's position requires a good amount upper body strength to move the round from the ready rack, flip the round 180 degrees and then push the round into the chamber of the main gun, within several seconds, in a limited amount of space.

The overall view of the interior of the M1A2 SEP turret with the gun elevated (top) and depressed (bottom) and ready to engage targets during a gunnery run. The bottom picture also shows the safety guards in position, which protects the crew from the recoil of the main gun, after firing.

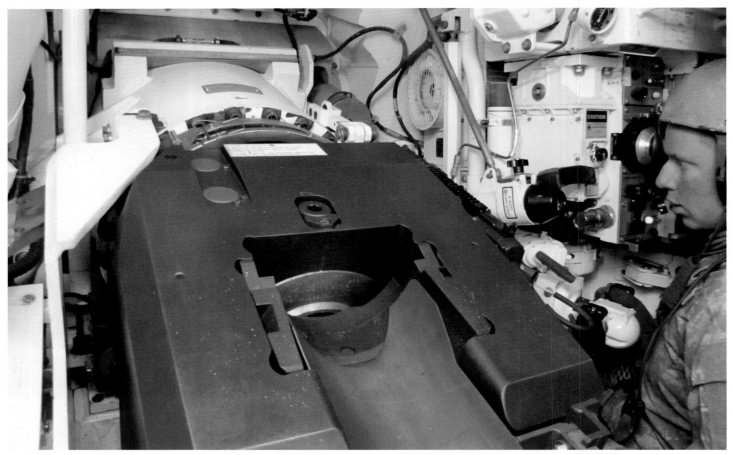

ABOVE: After returning to the baseline after their gunnery run, a gunner powers down the gunner's station, which includes the sights, power traverse and elevation. The main gun is elevated showing the top of the M265 breech and the accumulator reservoir, mounted on the turret roof and contains the hydraulic oil for the main gun's recoil system.

RIGHT: A tank commander and gunner scan downrange. They are not firing as there are no guards in place to protects the tank commander from the main gun recoil, which when fired, the breach moves 13 inches rearward.

ABOVE: C32, a 1-64 Armor M1A2 SEP waits in a laager site adjacent to the Red Cloud MPRC. BELOW: C-66, an M1A2 SEP from 2nd Battalion, 7 Infantry, 1st Armored Brigade Combat Team displays a damaged exhaust grille. Note that each of the combined arms battalions (2-7 Infantry, 1-64 Armor & 3-69 Armor) in the 1st ABCT has their rear bumper numbers in different locations, either on the engine deck or on the rear panel & infantry telephone box.

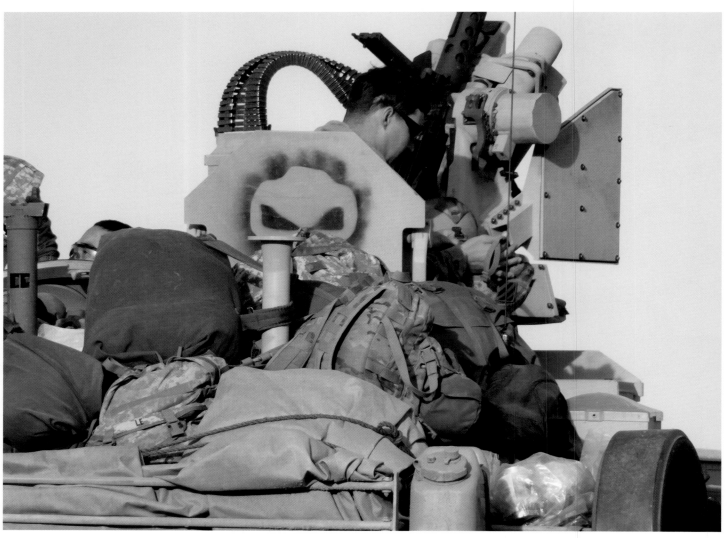

The Punisher graphic adorns the bore evacuator and tank commander's hatch of the tanks of 3d Platoon, C Company, 1-64 Armor. Note the mixture of crew bag types and camouflage, from plain green duffle bags to gray based Universal Pattern and the green and brown Objective Pattern assault packs in the top picture.

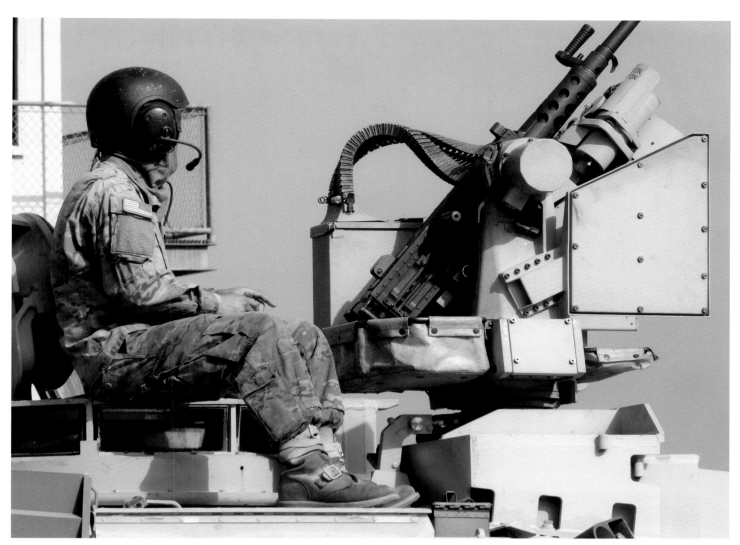

ABOVE: A tank commander awaits his tank's turn on the MPRC. The CROWS II mounts a newer M2A1 machine gun with its quick changing barrel handle. RIGHT: The crew load MG ammunition in preparation for their turn at gunnery. The ammunition storage bin on the CROWS II has greater capacity than the flexible mounted .50 Caliber machine gun, which is 100 rounds.

Field Exercises EAGER LION and SPARTAN SHIELD

A32, a M1A2 SEP from A Company, 3-8 Cavalry sits on the company tank line. It "wears" a M1 roller adapter mount and green replacement fenders. The crews commonly refer to this as the "bra." There are some Tank Urban Survivability Kit (TUSK) components installed on the turret, mainly the Loader's gun shield, Loader's protective armor and the Counter Sniper and Material Mount (CSAMM) above the main gun. This SEP has a M2A1 .50 caliber machine gun in the older flexible mount instead of a remote weapon station.

Various detail views of the M1 mine roller adapter, fitted via the upper and lower front towing points to A32. The tank conducts normal operations with only the adapter mounted. The two roller units are kept on a trailer in the unit trains and mounted with the assistance of a M88, when the unit anticipates contact with minefields.

An M88A2 Hercules uses a lifting sling to remove an AGT-1500 powerpack from a M1A2 SEP. The M88 operator will set the pack on a hard surface, usually the tank's engine deck or a similar surface, in this case a "liberated" USAF Cargo pallet to allow mechanics to work on the engine, transmission or both items.

Mechanics guide a M1A2 engine and transmission powerpack to the ground as a 3-8 Cavalry tank platoon goes through periodic maintenance services. The periodic services consist of removing the pack to check for leaks, cleaning air filters, changing hydraulic and oil filters, topping off fluids and cleaning the inside of the engine compartment in the hull.

A look at the forward part of the AGT-1500 turbine engine. The engine oil filter is the white cylinder on the left, with the tan starter immediately to the right. The hydro-mechanical unit (fuel pump) is to the right rear of the air intake screen. The engine and transmission oil cooler fans are outside of the silver engine exhaust duct.

Tank crewmembers prepare to clean the inside of the engine compartment by covering electrical plugs and other areas with trash bags to prevent damage from the upcoming pressure washing with water. Note the buildup of oil soaked dirt and dust that occurs during normal operations. This material causes a fire hazard that must be cleaned every time that the engine is removed.

Unit mechanics are removing a M1A2 SEP's powerpack in preparation for period maintenance services. Removing the pack consists of removing the engine deck, disconnecting the electrical connections, and unbolting the final drive connections. Lifting the pack out is a combination of lifting and moving rearward in a coordinate ballet between the M88 operator and the mechanics on the tank.

A M1A2 SEP undergoing services has broken torsion bar being removed from its suspension. The crew raised the roadwheel arms with a roadwheel arm lifter and removed the roadwheels as part of services. A M1A2 SEP tank can still operate with a broken torsion bar as long as bar is not on the #1 or #7 roadwheel arm. This tank is equipped with the newer "turbine" style plastic road wheel hubs.

An A Company 3-8 Cavalry tank is undergoing maintenance to replace a worn idler hub, shown in the inset picture below. The discoloration on the tow bar is from mounting in on the rear lifting eyes, resulting in the towing eye being in the path of the turbine exhaust. This could be an interesting effect to recreate on a model.

Uploading ammunition on a M1A2 SEP takes a full tank crew to accomplish. Two crewmembers will move the rounds from the ammunition pad to the tank, then hand the rounds up to another crew member on the tank, who hands the rounds down to the loader inside the turret, who places the rounds either in the tank's ready or semi-ready racks, in the bustle (rear part) of the turret.

OPPOSITE: The Breakfast of Champions." A tank crewman opens a Meal Ready to Eat and prepares to dine on the turret of a M1A2 SEP. Just visible to the right is the slotted barrel of the M2A1 .50 Cal. Machine Gun, mounted on the tank's Common Remotely Operated Weapons System (CROWS II). ABOVE: 1st Lieutenant Rodriquez, the Platoon Leader for A Company, 3-8 Cavalry, and PFC Hickernell pose with M865 Training Purpose Cone Stabilized Discarding Sabot – Tracer (TPCSDS-T) in front of an A Company tank. This tank has the Loader's gun shield mounted as well as a tow bar mounted on the front towing points.

Tank crewman of A Company, 3-8 Cavalry, 1st Cavalry Division pose with M865 TPCSDS-T rounds at the 3-8 Cavalry ammunition pad/ storage area. They are wearing OCP Combat shirts, which are worn in conjunction with the outer tactical vests aka body armor. The main gun rounds come in the green tubes in in background are for storing & transporting main gun ammunition.

2nd Lieutenant Jasmine Sanchez strikes a pose with a M865 TPCSDS-T round in the loader's position. 2LT Sanchez, a former enlisted finance specialist, is a newly commissioned field artillery officer, attached to A Company, 3-8 Cavalry, 1st Cavalry Division, during EAGER LION in Jordan and SPARTAN SHIELD in Kuwait.

ABOVE: Another tanks crew poses for a picture destined for Soldier of Fortune magazine. Carrying a round on one's shoulder is not the approved method of safeguarding main gun ammunition

BELOW: A college of pictures showing various tank crew members loading the main gun. The TPCSDS-T, shown in the pictures is an easier round to load as it is shorter, better balanced, and slightly lighter than the heavier, longer, M831A1 Training Purpose - Tracer (TP-T) round, which replicates the weight and ballistic trajectory of the M830 High Explosive Anti-Tank-Tracer (HEAT-T) round.